The High IQ Society

BOOST YOUR IQ

THIS IS A SEVENOAKS BOOK

This edition first published in Great Britain in 2016 by SevenOaks
An imprint of the Carlton Publishing Group
20 Mortimer Street
London W1T 3JW

A CIP catalogue for this book is available from the British Library.

ISBN 978-1-78177-470-0

Printed in the UK

10 9 8 7 6 5 4 3 2

Mensa
The High IQ Society

BOOST YOUR IQ

Hundreds of challenging puzzles

Harold Gale and Carolyn Skitt

SEVENOAKS

WHAT IS MENSA?

Mensa is the international society for people with a high IQ.
We have more than 100,000 members in over 40 countries worldwide.

The society's aims are:
> to identify and foster human intelligence for the benefit of humanity
> to encourage research in the nature, characteristics, and uses of intelligence
> to provide a stimulating intellectual and social environment for its members

Anyone with an IQ score in the top two per cent of population is eligible to become a member of Mensa – are you the 'one in 50' we've been looking for?

Mensa membership offers an excellent range of benefits:
> Networking and social activities nationally and around the world
> Special Interest Groups – hundreds of chances to pursue your hobbies
> and interests – from art to zoology!
> Monthly members' magazine and regional newsletters
> Local meetings – from games challenges to food and drink
> National and international weekend gatherings and conferences
> Intellectually stimulating lectures and seminars
> Access to the worldwide SIGHT network for travellers and hosts

For more information about Mensa: www.mensa.org.uk, or

British Mensa Ltd.,
St John's House,
St John's Square,
Wolverhampton
WV2 4AH
Telephone: +44 (0) 1902 772771
E-mail: enquiries@mensa.org.uk

CONTENTS

INTRODUCTION

Intelligence, to a greater or lesser degree, is found in all humans. Your level of intelligence is the same throughout your life. Many people however, fail to reach their true potential and this is the rationale behind this book.

The tests in the book are fun tests. They begin on an easy plane and gradually rise to a more difficult one. The tests measure speed and accuracy of thought and should be regarded as a form of mental jogging. Many people take physical exercise but not so many mental exercise. Now is your chance.

Mensa has put together this series of puzzles to challenge your thinking and to help exercise your brain. In each test the correct answer is to be found in one of the shapes. Proceed through each test as quickly as possible and first answer those questions you find easiest. Then return to the more difficult ones. Check your answers when the time is up, total the correct answers and see how well you did on the results table. Don't be downhearted if you didn't get a high score – there's always room for improvement!

Whatever your score, it is always a good idea to find out what your real I.Q. is – after all, we measure our bodies, why not our minds?

TEST 1

1 Which of the numbers should replace the question mark?

A	B	C	D
3	5	1	9
2	0	4	6
7	1	0	8
2	3	1	?

8 | 2
A | B

9 | 1
C | D

4 | 6
E | F

TEST 1

2 Each same symbol has a value. Work out the logic and discover what should replace the question mark.

TEST 1 time limit 20 minutes

Z	Z	Ψ	Ω	**?**
Ξ	Ξ	Ξ	Ξ	**8**
Ψ	Z	Ψ	Ω	**16**
Ψ	Z	Ψ	Ξ	**13**
13	**11**	**14**	**14**	

6 A	**12** B	**7** C
15 D	**10** E	**9** F

TEST 1

Here is an unusual safe. Each of the buttons must be pressed only once in the correct order to open it. The last button is marked F. The number of moves and the direction is marked on each button. Thus 1U would mean one move up, while 1L would mean one move to the left. Using the grid reference, which button is the first you must press?

TEST 1 time limit 20 minutes

	A	B	C	D	E
	3R	4D	2L	2L	2D
	3R	3R	3D	2L	2D
	1R	1D	F	3L	2L
	2U	1L	3U	1U	2L
	4R	1L	1R	1U	4U

5D	3C
A	B

1A	4E
C	D

1B	2C
E	F

TEST 1

4 Insert the correct mathematical signs between each number in order to resolve the equation. What are the signs?

| 11 | | 3 | | 7 | = | 21 |

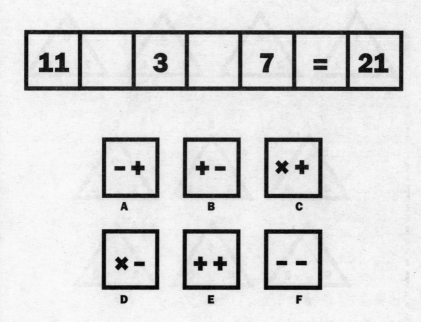

A − +

B + −

C ✖ +

D ✖ −

E + +

F − −

TEST 1

5 Which triangle continues this series?

TEST 1

6 Discover the connection between the letters and the numbers. Which number should replace the question mark?

TEST 1 time limit 20 minutes

G	7
M	13
U	21
J	10
W	?

14	23	9
A	B	C
26	2	11
D	E	F

TEST 1

7 Which of the constructed boxes
cannot be made from the pattern?

14

TEST 1

8 Which of the numbers should replace the question mark?

3	4	1	2
5	2	2	1
1	1	1	7
1	2	6	?

3 **A**	5 **B**
1 **C**	6 **D**
2 **E**	4 **F**

TEST 1

9 Which of the clocks continues this series?

TEST 1 time limit 20 minutes

TEST 1

TEST 1 time limit 20 minutes

(2) A   (5) B

(7) C   (6) D

(4) E   (9) F

TEST 1

11 Move from ring to touching ring, starting from the bottom left corner and finishing in the top right corner. Collect nine numbers and total them. Which is the highest possible total?

TEST 1

12 This square follows a logical pattern. Which of the tiles should be used to complete the square?

TEST 1 time limit 20 minutes

TEST 1

13 Which of the slices should be used to complete the cake?

TEST 1 time limit 20 minutes

TEST 1

Each straight line of five numbers should total 20. Which of the numbers will replace the question mark?

TEST 1 time limit 20 minutes

5	2		2	5
1		?		1
5	8	4		3
	2	2	2	8
3	2	2	10	3

4 A	1 B
3 C	6 D
5 E	2 F

TEST 1

15 Start at any corner and follow the lines. Collect another four numbers and total the five. One of the numbers in the squares below can be used to complete the diagram. If the correct one has been chosen, one of the routes involving it will give a total of 28. Which one is it?

TEST 1 time limit 20 minutes

TEST 2

1 Which of the boxes should be used to replace the question mark?

TEST 2 time limit 20 minutes

TEST 2

2 Scales one and two are in perfect balance. Which of these pans should replace the empty one?

TEST 2 time limit 20 minutes

TEST 2

3 How many ways are there to score 25 on this dartboard using three darts only? Each dart always lands in a sector and no dart falls to the floor.

TEST 2 time limit 20 minutes

TEST 2

4 Which square's contents matches D1?

TEST 2

5 Which of the numbers should logically replace the question mark in the octagon?

TEST 2 time limit 20 minutes

27

TEST 2

6 Which number is missing from this series?

TEST 2 time limit 20 minutes

TEST 2

7 Complete the square using the five numbers shown. When completed no row, column or diagonal line will use the same number more than once. What should replace the question mark?

1	2	3	4	5
4	5	1	2	3
?				

1
A

5
B

2
C

3
D

4
E

TEST 2

8 Which of the numbers should replace the question mark?

6	3	1	4	9
5	1	0	2	8
1	2	1	2	?

3	4
A	B
6	1
C	D
8	2
E	F

TEST 2

9 Start at 1 and move from circle to touching circle. Collect four numbers each time. How many different routes are there to collect 11? A reversed route counts twice.

TEST 2 time limit 20 minutes

```
            2
         2  2  2
      2  3  5  5  5
   5  5  3  1  2  2  2
      3  3  3  5  5
         5  3  3
            2
```

```
   2     3
   A     B

   6     4
   C     D

   5     7
   E     F
```

TEST 2

10 Here is an unusual safe. Each of the buttons must be pressed only once in the correct order to open it. The last button is marked F. The number of moves and the direction is marked on each button. Thus 1i would mean one move in, whilst 1o would mean one move out. 1c would mean one move clockwise and 1a would mean one move anti-clockwise. Which button is the first you must press?

TEST 2 time limit 20 minutes

TEST 2

11 Which of the numbers should replace the question mark?

6	3	1	8
5	4	2	7
0	9	4	5
7	2	8	?

6
A

3
W

2
C

4
D

1
E

5
F

TEST 2

12 Which triangle continues this series?

TEST 2 time limit 20 minutes

TEST 2

13 Insert the correct mathematical signs between each number in order to resolve the equation. What are the signs?

13		2		4	=	7

A + −

B × +

C − −

D × ×

E ÷ ×

F − ×

TEST 2

14 Discover the connection between the letters and the numbers. Which number should replace the question mark?

TEST 2 time limit 20 minutes

C	3	14	N
Y	25	12	L
F	6	19	S
U	21	16	P
O			D

15	4
A	

5	26
B	

11	18
C	

24	8
D	

13	3
E	

1	19
F	

36

TEST 2

15 Which of the constructed boxes can be made from the pattern?

TEST 3

1 Each same symbol has a value. Work out the logic and discover what should replace the question mark.

TEST 3 time limit 25 minutes

α	α	α	α	16
β	β	δ	χ	?
δ	α	δ	α	
α	β	χ	χ	21

      22   25

25 A   **21** B   **27** C

28 D   **29** E   **23** F

TEST 3

2 Scales one and two are in perfect balance. Which of these pans should replace the empty one?

TEST 3

3 When rearranged the shapes will give a number. Which of the numbers is it?

TEST 3 time limit 25 minutes

(6) A
(7) B
(9) C
(3) D
(8) E
(4) F

TEST 3

4   Which of the numbers should replace the question mark?

6	1	7	3
2	5	2	8
3	5	5	1
4	4	1	?

6	3
A	B

4	2
C	D

5	1
E	F

TEST 3

5 Here is an unusual safe. Each of the buttons must be pressed only once in the correct order to open it. The last button is marked F. The number of moves and the direction is marked on each button. Thus 1i would mean one move in, whilst 1o would mean one move out. 1c would mean one move clock-wise and 1a would mean one move anti-clockwise. Which button is the first you must press?

TEST 3

6 Which number is missing from this series?

TEST 3

7 Which triangle should replace the empty one?

44

TEST 3

8 Which of the numbers should logically replace the question mark in the octagon?

45

TEST 3

9 Which square's contents matches C4?

TEST 3

10 How many ways are there to score 123 on this dartboard using three darts only? Each dart always lands in a sector and no dart falls to the floor. Any sector can be used more than once in any set of throws, but the same set of numbers can be used in one order only.

TEST 3

11 Here is an unusual safe. Each of the buttons must be pressed only once in the correct order to open it. The last button is marked F. The number of moves and the direction is marked on each button. Thus 1U would mean one move up, while 1L would mean one move to the left. Using the grid reference, which button is the first you must press?

TEST 3 time limit 25 minutes

	A	B	C	D	E	F
1	2D	4R	F	4D	3D	4D
2	3D	2D	3R	1R	3D	5L
3	5R	1U	2U	2L	1L	3L
4	3U	1R	1D	3U	1L	5L
5	1R	4U	3U	3U	2U	1U

4B	5F
A	B
2C	1E
C	D
4D	3A
E	F

48

TEST 3

12 Which of the numbers should logically replace the question mark in the octagon?

TEST 3

13 Which of the numbers should replace the question mark?

TEST 3 time limit 25 minutes

1	0	3	4
8	4	2	6
6	2	3	7
9	5	2	?

6 **A**	9 **B**
5 **C**	3 **D**
2 **E**	7 **F**

50

TEST 3

14 Which of the boxes should be used to replace the question mark?

TEST 3

15 Which of the numbers should replace the question mark?

TEST 3 time limit 25 minutes

2	1	2	1	?
5	1	2	7	3
7	2	4	8	6

8	1
A	B
7	9
C	D
3	4
E	F

TEST 3

16 This square follows a logical pattern. Which of the tiles should be used to complete the square?

TEST 3

17 Which of the constructed boxes cannot be made from the pattern?

54

TEST 3

18 Move from ring to touching ring, starting from the bottom left corner and finishing in the top right corner. Collect nine numbers and total them. Which is the highest possible total?

TEST 3

19 Scales one and two are in perfect balance. Which of the pans should replace the empty one?

TEST 3 time limit 25 minutes

TEST 3

20 Which of the clocks continues this series?

TEST 4

1 Insert the correct mathematical signs between each number in order to resolve the equation. What are the signs?

9		3		17	=	44

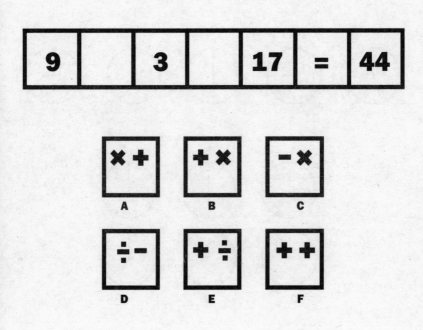

A × +

B + ×

C − ×

D ÷ −

E + ÷

F + +

TEST 4

2   Start at 1 and move from circle to touching circle. Collect four numbers each time. How many different routes are there to collect 12? A reversed route counts twice.

TEST 4 time limit 25 minutes

```
            2
        3   3   2
      3   6   6   6   2
    6   2   3   1   3   6   3
      3   6   2   3   3
        6   6   2
            2
```

12	9
A	B
8	7
C	D
11	3
E	F

TEST 4

3 Which triangle belongs to this series?

TEST 4

4 Which of the clocks continues this series?

A   B   C

D   E   F

TEST 4

5 Which of the numbers should replace the question mark?

	A	B	C	D
	7	9	8	8
	3	9	5	7
	1	6	3	4
	2	2	1	?

4	2
A	B
3	1
C	D
5	6
E	F

TEST 4

6 Here is an unusual safe. Each of the buttons must be pressed only once in the correct order to open it. The last button is marked F. The number of moves and the direction is marked on each button. Thus 1U would mean one move up, while 1L would mean one move to the left. Using the grid reference, which button is the first you must press?

	A	B	C	D	E
1	2R	2R	4D	1D	4L
2	1D	1U	F	3D	3L
3	3R	1R	1D	1R	3L
4	4R	1D	1R	2L	3U
5	1U	3R	3U	3L	3U

2C A	1E B
4D C	3E D
2A E	5B F

TEST 4

7 Start at any corner and follow the lines. Collect another four numbers and total the five. One of the numbers in the squares below can be used to complete the diagram. If the correct one has been chosen, one of the routes involving it will give a total of 33. Which one is it?

TEST 4 time limit 25 minutes

TEST 4

8 This square follows a logical pattern. Which of the tiles should be used to complete the square?

5	3	1	3	1
3	5	5	1	5
	5	3	1	5
	1	1	3	5
1	5	5	5	3

A
1
3

B
5
2

C
3
5

D
5
1

E
1
2

F
1
1

TEST 4

9 Move from ring to touching ring, starting from the bottom left corner and finishing in the top right corner. Collect nine numbers and total them. Which is the highest possible total?

TEST 4

10 When rearranged the shapes will give a number. Which of the numbers is it?

8 A

3 B

5 C

2 D

1 E

9 F

TEST 4

11 Which square's contents matches D1?

	A	B	C	D	
	3 3	2	2	4	1
	2	1 1	2 2	2 1	
	4 4	2	2	3 3	2
	3	4 4	4 1	4	
	3	3	1	4 4	3
	2 2	1 1	3 3	4	
	3	2 2	1	2 2	4
	3 3	4	1 1	1	

A4	**B2**
A	B
C1	**C2**
C	D
A1	**D3**
E	F

TEST 4

12 How many ways are there to score 60 on this dartboard using three darts only? Each dart always lands in a sector and no dart falls to the floor.

TEST 4 time limit 25 minutes

TEST 4

13 Each same symbol has a value. Work out the logic and discover what should replace the question mark.

TEST 4 time limit 25 minutes

α	β	α	β	18
β	χ	δ	α	
χ	χ	β	β	20
χ	δ	δ	δ	?

23   22

37 A	**30** B	**28** C
35 D	**24** E	**39** F

TEST 4

14 Which of the boxes should be used to replace the question mark?

TEST 4

15 Complete the square using the five numbers shown. When completed no row, column or diagonal line will use the same number more than once. What should replace the question mark?

1	2	3	4	5
		5		
?		2		
		4		
4	5	1	2	3

2   4
A   B

3   5
C   D

1
E

TEST 4

16 Which circle should replace the empty one?

TEST 4

17 Each straight line of five numbers should total 25. Which of the numbers will replace the question mark?

TEST 4 time limit 25 minutes

?	2		1	
2		7		1
			1	2
4	2	3	3	
3	5	3	12	2

8	6
A	B

12	10
C	D

2	15
E	F

TEST 4

18 Which of the slices should be
used to replace the question mark and
complete the cake?

TEST 4 time limit 25 minutes

TEST 4

19 Which of the numbers should replace the question mark?

5	9	1	2	1
8	9	6	4	3
3	0	5	2	?

9	6
A	B
2	7
C	D
4	5
E	F

TEST 4

20 Discover the connection between the letters and the numbers. Which number should replace the question mark?

S	?	K
E	516	P
Z	262	B
I	914	N
A	120	T

393	671	385
A	**B**	**C**
5482	1911	2363
D	**E**	**F**

TEST 5

1 Here is an unusual safe. Each of the buttons must be pressed only once in the correct order to open it. The last button is marked F. The number of moves and the direction is marked on each button. Thus 1i would mean one move in, while 1o would mean one move out. 1c would mean one move clock-wise and 1a would mean one move anti-clockwise. Which button is the first you must press?

TEST 5 time limit 40 minutes

TEST 5

2 Complete the square using the five symbols shown. When completed no row, column or diagonal line will use the same symbol more than once. What should replace the question mark?

TEST 5

3 Which of the slices should be used to complete the cake?

TEST 5

4   Start at 4 and move from circle to touching circle. Collect four numbers each time. How many different routes are there to collect 24? A reversed route counts twice.

TEST 5 time limit 40 minutes

```
          5
       7  7  8
    5  8  5  8  7
  8  8  8  4  5  8  5
    7  7  8  5  5
       5  8  8
          7
```

```
    2     3
    A     B

    4     5
    C     D

    6     7
    E     F
```

TEST 5

5   Each straight line of five numbers should total 30. Which of the numbers will replace the question mark?

TEST 5 time limit 40 minutes

8				10
4	7	10		
7	8	6	4	5
		2	5	11
2		?	12	4

15
A

13
B

19
C

14
D

16
E

3
F

TEST 5

6 Which number is missing from this series?

TEST 5

7 Complete the square using the five symbols shown. When completed no row, column or diagonal line will use the same symbol more than once. What should replace the question mark?

A   B

C   D

E

84

TEST 5

TEST 5 time limit 40 minutes

TEST 5

9 Which square's contents matches C1?

	A		B		C		D		
	A	E	A	A	A	A	B	B	1
	B	D	A	A	B	D	A	B	
	D	E	E	E	B	C	B	B	2
	B	B	E	E	E	A	B	C	
	D	D	C	A	C	C	A	B	3
	A	D	C	B	E	E	C	D	
	B	E	A	E	B	A	D	D	4
	D	C	E	D	A	D	C	D	

Options:

- **4A** — A
- **2D** — B
- **4C** — C
- **1B** — D
- **3B** — E
- **1D** — F

TEST 5

10 How many ways are there to score 62 on this dartboard using four darts only? Each dart always lands in a sector and no dart falls to the floor.

TEST 5 time limit 40 minutes

TEST 5

11 Which of the numbers should logically replace the question mark in the octagon?

TEST 5

12 This square follows a logical pattern. Which of the tiles should be used to complete the square?

TEST 5 time limit 40 minutes

TEST 5

13 Each letter has a value. Work out the logic and discover what should replace the question mark.

A	B	C	D	5
E	F	G	H	11
I	J	K	L	32
M	N	O	P	?

22	14	20	30

45	A	12	B	26	C

38	D	34	E	21	F

TEST 5

14 Here is an unusual safe. Each of the buttons must be pressed only once in the correct order to open it. The last button is marked F. The number of moves and the direction is marked on each button. Thus 1U would mean one move up, while 1L would mean one move to the left. Using the grid reference, which button is the first you must press?

TEST 5 time limit 40 minutes

	A	B	C	D	E	F
1	4D	3R	3D	2R	4L	3L
2	3R	3R	1L	3D	1D	5L
3	1R	2D	1U	1L	4L	1D
4	1R	2R	1D	1U	4L	2U
5	4R	4U	F	4U	1R	2U

2F **A**	5C **B**
4D **C**	5B **D**
4E **E**	3F **F**

TEST 5

15 Move from ring to touching ring, starting from the bottom left corner and finishing in the top right corner. Collect nine numbers and total them. Which is the highest possible total?

A 49   B 50   C 55   D 41   E 47   F 35

TEST 5

16 Which of the numbers should replace the question mark?

	A	B	C	D
	8	3	4	1
	6	1	2	3
	9	2	0	7
	5	1	1	?

7	4
A	B

1	6
C	D

3	9
E	F

TEST 5

17 Start at any corner and follow the lines. Collect another four numbers and total the five. One of the numbers in the squares below can be used to complete the diagram. If the correct one has been chosen, one of the routes involving it will give a total of 20. Which one is it?

94

TEST 5

18 Scales one and two are in perfect balance. Which of these pans should replace the empty one?

TEST 5 time limit 40 minutes

TEST 5

19 Here is an unusual safe. Each of the buttons must be pressed only once in the correct order to open it. The last button is marked F. The number of moves and the direction is marked on each button. Thus 1i would mean one move in, while 1o would mean one move out. 1c would mean one move clock-wise and 1a would mean one move anti-clockwise. Which button is the first you must press?

TEST 5

20 Insert the correct mathematical signs between each number in order to resolve the equation. What are the signs?

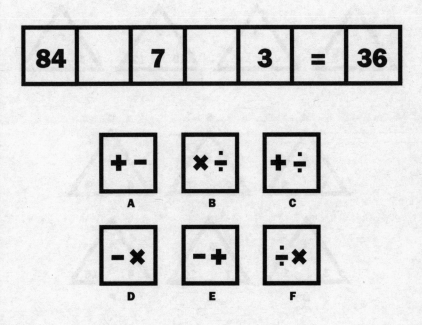

| 84 | | 7 | | 3 | = | 36 |

A + −

B × ÷

C + ÷

D − ×

E − +

F ÷ ×

TEST 5

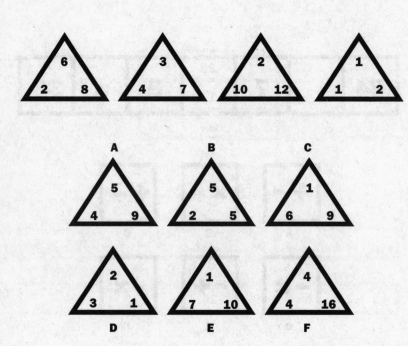

Series triangles:

| 6 | 3 | 2 | 1 |
| 2 8 | 4 7 | 10 12 | 1 2 |

Options:

A: 5 / 4 9
B: 5 / 2 5
C: 1 / 6 9
D: 2 / 3 1
E: 1 / 7 10
F: 4 / 4 16

TEST 5

22 Discover the connection between the letters and the numbers. Which number should replace the question mark?

C	23	T
J	17	G
L	34	V
E	10	E
A	?	X

13	**21**	**25**
A	B	C
33	**26**	**28**
D	E	F

TEST 5

23 Which of the clocks continues this series?

TEST 5

24 Which of the numbers should replace the question mark?

TEST 5 time limit 40 minutes

9	7	8	5
3	1	4	3
8	8	7	6
2	2	3	?

1 A	**6** B
2 C	**5** D
3 E	**4** F

TEST 5

25 Which of the constructed boxes can be made from the pattern?

102

TEST 5

26 When rearranged the shapes will give a letter. Which of the letters is it?

R A
D B
K C
J D
L E
S F

TEST 5

27 Start at 4 and move from circle to touching circle. Collect four numbers each time. How many different routes are there to collect 10? A reversed route counts twice.

TEST 5 time limit 40 minutes

```
              1
          3   3   2
        1   3   2   3   1
      1   1   2   4   2   3   2
        2   1   3   2   2
          1   3   1
              3
```

12	8
A	**B**
5	10
C	**D**
6	11
E	**F**

TEST 5

28 Each straight line of five numbers should total 50. Which of the numbers will replace the question mark?

12	10	14		12
7	14	14	14	1
12	18			8
11			?	21
8	2		26	8

6	4
A	B

12	10
C	D

8	2
E	F

TEST 5

29 Which of the boxes should be used to replace the question mark?

TEST 5

30 Each straight line of five numbers should total 35. Only two numbers must be used to complete the square. Which of the numbers will replace the question mark?

9	8	11	0	
1	11	11	9	
	11	?		
11	5			13
	0		20	5

12 **A**	9 **B**
1 **C**	10 **D**
7 **E**	4 **F**

107

TEST 6

1 Which of the slices should be
used to complete the cake?

TEST 6

2 Start at any corner and follow the lines. Collect another four numbers and total the five. One of the numbers in the squares below can be used to complete the diagram. If the correct one has been chosen, one of the routes involving it will give a total of 41. Which one is it?

TEST 6

3 When rearranged the shapes will give a letter. Which of the letters is it?

Y M
A B

T V
C D

A X
E F

TEST 6

4 Each straight line of five numbers should total 40. Only two numbers are used to complete the square. Which of the numbers will replace the question mark?

TEST 6 time limit 45 minutes

			2	
12				0
	?	8	6	6
3	7	6	7	17
6	5	6	16	7

4 A	**10** B
13 C	**21** D
18 E	**5** F

TEST 6

5 Here is an unusual safe. Each of the buttons must be pressed only once in the correct order to open it. The last button is marked F. The number of moves and the direction is marked on each button. Thus 1i would mean one move in, while 1o would mean one move out. 1c would mean one move clockwise and 1a would mean one move anti-clockwise. Which button is the first you must press?

TEST 6 time limit 45 minutes

TEST 6

6 Scales one and two are in perfect balance. Which of these pans should replace the empty one?

TEST 6

7 Which of the slices should be used to complete the cake?

TEST 6

8 Which of the numbers should replace the question mark?

TEST 6 time limit 45 minutes

6	3	9	4	1
5	8	7	6	3
?	5	1	7	8

3 A	5 B
8 C	7 D
2 E	0 F

TEST 6

9 Which arrow is missing from this series?

TEST 6

10 Move from ring to touching ring, starting from the bottom left corner and finishing in the top right corner. Collect nine numbers and total them. Which is the highest possible total?

117

TEST 6

11 This square follows a logical pattern. Which of the tiles should be used to complete the square?

TEST 6 time limit 45 minutes

TEST 6

12 Which square's contents matches D4?

	A		B		C		D		
	1	1	5	1	3	1	1	3	**1**
	5	5	2	3	2	3	5	4	
	2	3	4	4	4	2	3	3	**2**
	4	3	1	4	2	5	4	5	
	3	3	1	4	4	4	2	5	**3**
	4	3	2	5	1	1	4	3	
	3	4	5	3	4	2	3	5	**4**
	2	2	4	4	3	1	1	2	

A2	C1
A	B
D3	C3
C	D
B4	B1
E	F

TEST 6

13 How many ways are there to score 85 on this dartboard using four darts only? Each dart always lands in a sector and no dart falls to the floor.

TEST 6 time limit 45 minutes

TEST 6

14 Which of the numbers should logically replace the question mark in the octagon?

TEST 6

15 Which circle should replace the empty one?

8 3
A B

6 1
C D

5 2
E F

TEST 6

16 Complete the square using the five numbers shown. When completed no row, column or diagonal line will use the same number more than once. What should replace the question mark?

1	2			
4	5			
2	3			
				?

4	5
A	B

1	2
C	D

3
E

TEST 6

17 Discover the connection between the letters and the numbers. Which number should replace the question mark?

TEST 6 time limit 45 minutes

A	1	B
D	7	K
Q	2	O
R	2	T
Z	?	C

12	5	20
A	B	C

28	23	9
D	E	F

TEST 6

18 Which triangle belongs to this series?

TEST 6 time limit 45 minutes

TEST 6

19 Each same symbol has a value. Work out the logic and discover what should replace the question mark.

TEST 6 time limit 45 minutes

Κ	Κ	Λ	Λ	46
Λ	Κ	Κ	Ο	
Ο	Ο	Π	Π	62
Λ	Λ	Κ	Ο	
50	49		?	

48	A	58	B	50	C

42	D	49	E	47	F

TEST 6

TEST 6 time limit 45 minutes

20 Which of the numbers should replace the question mark?

2	3	2	8
1	8	1	9
3	0	3	3
1	1	4	?

2
A

1
B

4
C

5
D

8
E

7
F

TEST 6

21 Which of the clocks continues
this series?

A   B   C

D   E   F

TEST 6

22 Which of the constructed boxes cannot be made from the pattern?

TEST 6

23 Which of the slices should be used to complete the cake?

TEST 6

24 Which of the boxes should be used to replace the question mark?

TEST 6

25 Insert the correct mathematical signs between each number in order to resolve the equation. What are the signs?

TEST 6 time limit 45 minutes

8		7		3		1		19	=	76

× - ÷ +

A

+ ÷ - ×

B

÷ - + ×

C

÷ + × -

D

- × - +

E

÷ × ÷ ×

F

TEST 6

26 Here is an unusual safe. Each of the buttons must be pressed only once in the correct order to open it. The last button is marked F. The number of moves and the direction is marked on each button. Thus 1U would mean one move up, while 1L would mean one move to the left. Using the grid reference, which button is the first you must press?

	A	B	C	D	E	F
1	1R	3D	1R	4D	5D	1L
2	2D	3R	1R	2D	4L	4L
3	F	1R	2U	2L	4L	2U
4	1D	4R	2D	1U	2L	2D
5	5R	1D	1L	1R	1U	2U
6	5U	2R	1U	3L	3U	4U

A	B
6B	2C

C	D
6D	3E

E	F
2F	4A

TEST 6

27 Move from ring to touching ring, starting from the bottom left corner and finishing in the top right corner. Collect nine numbers and total them. Which is the highest possible total?

TEST 6 time limit 45 minutes

TEST 6

 28 Which square's contents matches B1?

TEST 6

Which arrow is missing from this series?

TEST 6 time limit 45 minutes

TEST 6

30 How many ways are there to score 58 on this dartboard using four darts only? Each dart always lands in a sector and no dart falls to the floor.

TEST 7

1 Which triangle belongs to this series?

TEST 7

2 Start at 15 and move from circle to touching circle. Collect four numbers each time. How many different routes are there to collect 50? A reversed route counts twice.

TEST 7 time limit 1 hour

```
              10
          10  10   5
      10  20  20   5  20
   5  20  10  15   5   5  20
      20  10  10  10  10
           5  20   5
               5
```

5	2
A	B
3	6
C	D
7	8
E	F

TEST 7

3 Which of the numbers should replace the question mark?

2	2	5	7	0
4	9	5	7	?
7	2	1	4	6

1	3
A	B

8	9
C	D

6	4
E	F

TEST 7

4 Which of the numbers should logically replace the question mark in the octagon?

TEST 7

5 Complete the square using the five symbols shown. When completed no row, column or diagonal line will use the same symbol more than once. What should replace the question mark?

TEST 7

6 Here is an unusual safe. Each of the buttons must be pressed only once in the correct order to open it. The last button is marked F. The number of moves and the direction is marked on each button. Thus 1U would mean one move up, whilst 1L would mean one move to the left. Using the grid reference, which button is the first you must press?

TEST 7 time limit 1 hour

	A	B	C	D	E	F
1	F	4D	6D	2L	2D	5L
2	4D	2R	3D	2R	4L	4D
3	2D	3D	2U	3L	1R	3L
4	4R	1U	1R	3U	2D	3U
5	1U	1U	1R	2U	2D	1L
6	3R	1R	4U	1D	5U	1U
7	1R	5U	2L	2R	5U	3U

2B	7D
A	B

1F	4C
C	D

6A	3E
E	F

TEST 7

7 Which of the boxes should be used to replace the question mark?

TEST 7

8 Which of the numbers should replace the question mark?

8	4	2	2	4
9	1	1	2	2
?	2	1	0	2

9 A	**3** B
6 C	**5** D
8 E	**7** F

145

TEST 7

9 When rearranged the shapes will give a letter. Which of the letters is it?

(U) (W)
A   B

(V) (N)
C   D

(B) (C)
E   F

TEST 7

10 When the tiles in this square are rearranged a logical pattern will emerge. Which of the tiles should be used to complete the square?

TEST 7 time limit 1 hour

3	1	1	2	2
3	1	2	1	1
3		1	1	2
1		2	2	3
2	3	2	2	2

2 3 **A**	2 2 **B**
4 1 **C**	1 1 **D**
1 4 **E**	5 1 **F**

147

TEST 7

11 How many ways are there to score 99 on this dartboard using five darts only? Each dart always lands in a sector and no dart falls to the floor.

TEST 7 time limit 1 hour

TEST 7

12 Which square's contents matches A4?

TEST 7 time limit 1 hour

	A	B	C	D	
1	+ ■ ✱ / ● ▲ –	■ ● – / + ✱ ■	● ✱ + / + ■ ▲	● + – / – ✱ ■	**1**
2	✱ ● + / + ■ –	– ✱ ■ / + – –	✱ – ✱ / ▲ ● +	– + + / ▲ ● ✱	**2**
3	▲ – ✱ / – + ●	● + ✱ / – ▲ ●	■ ● ■ / ● ■ ●	+ ■ + / ● ▲ –	**3**
4	+ ● ✱ / ▲ ✱ –	– ✱ ■ / + + ▲	– ● – / + ■ ▲	+ ✱ ✱ / ✱ ▲ ■	**4**

D3 A	**B4** B
C2 C	**A1** D
B1 E	**A3** F

149

TEST 7

13 Which shape is missing from this series?

TEST 7

14 Which triangle should replace the empty one?

TEST 7

15 Insert the correct mathematical signs between each number in order to resolve the equation. What are the signs?

TEST 7 time limit 1 hour

28		4		8		21		5	=	58

− × + −	× + − +	+ × + ×
A	**B**	**C**

÷ + + −	− ÷ × −	× − ÷ +
D	**E**	**F**

TEST 7

16 Which of the constructed boxes cannot be made from the pattern?

TEST 7

17 Which triangle continues this series?

6
11 19

12
15 16

24
19 13

48
23 10

A
20
13 10

B
96
28 40

C
23
6 72

D
96
19 8

E
96
27 7

F
50
15 45

TEST 7

18 Which of the slices should be used to complete the cake?

155

TEST 7

TEST 7 time limit 1 hour

19 Each straight line of five numbers should total 45. Which of the numbers will replace the question mark?

11	12	13	0	
8	13	13	11	0
11	13			3
6				
	0	?	24	

5 **A**	2 **B**
3 **C**	4 **D**
1 **E**	6 **F**

TEST 7

20 Here is an unusual safe. Each of the buttons must be pressed only once in the correct order to open it. The last button is marked F. The number of moves and the direction is marked on each button. Thus 1i would mean one move in, whilst 1o would mean one move out. 1c would mean one move clockwise and 1a would mean one move anti-clockwise. Which button is the first you must press?

TEST 7

21 Each same symbol has a value. Work out the logic and discover what should replace the question mark.

TEST 7 time limit 1 hour

φ	φ	φ	γ	?
γ	γ	γ	η	29
τ	τ	τ	η	68
η	η	φ	γ	

41   30

35 A	**20** B	**25** C

27 D	**31** E	**32** F

158

TEST 7

22 This square follows a logical pattern. Which of the tiles should be used to complete the square?

TEST 7

23 When rearranged the shapes will give a number. Which of the numbers is it?

TEST 7 time limit 1 hour

TEST 7

24 Scales one and two are in perfect balance. Which of these pans should replace the empty one?

TEST 7

25 Start at any corner and follow the lines. Collect another four numbers and total the five. One of the numbers in the squares below can be used to complete the diagram. If the correct one has been chosen, one of the routes involving it will give a total of 45. Which one is it?

TEST 7

26 Which of the numbers should
replace the question mark?

TEST 7 time limit 1 hour

	A	B	C	D
	4	2	7	1
	1	9	5	4
	3	5	8	7
	2	7	6	?

8	2
A	B
9	1
C	D
6	5
E	F

TEST 7

27 Insert the correct mathematical signs between each number in order to resolve the equation. What are the signs?

TEST 7 time limit 1 hour

| 9 | | 4 | | 2 | | 17 | | 16 | = | 18 |

+ ÷ - ×	× × ÷ ÷	÷ × - +
A	**B**	**C**

× - ÷ +	+ + - ×	- - × +
D	**E**	**F**

TEST 7

28 Which of the constructed boxes can be made from the pattern?

TEST 7

29 Discover the connection between the letters and the numbers. Which number should replace the question mark?

TEST 7 time limit 1 hour

F	136	M
U	421	D
H	178	Q
O	115	A
X	?	I

672	834	411
A	B	C

295	118	924
D	E	F

TEST 7

30 Which of the clocks continues this series?

TEST 8

1 Which of the numbers should logically replace the question mark in the octagon?

TEST 8 time limit 1 hour

TEST 8

2 Complete the square using the five numbers shown. When completed no row, column or diagonal line will use the same number more than once. Which can logically replace the question mark?

5	2	4	3	
1				
		?		

5
A

2
B

1
C

3
D

4
E

TEST 8

3 Start at 3 and move from circle to touching circle. Collect four numbers each time. How many different routes are there to collect 13? A reversed route counts twice.

TEST 8 time limit 1 hour

```
          5
       5  4  5
    1  1  1  5  4
  1  4  1  3  5  5  1
     4  4  4  1  1
        5  4  1
           4
```

```
  1        5
  A        B

  3        6
  C        D

  7        4
  E        F
```

TEST 8

4 Which of the numbers should replace the question mark?

9	5	4	8	1
8	9	6	3	1
7	5	?	2	3

3	2
A	**B**

6	9
C	**D**

5	1
E	**F**

TEST 8

5 Here is an unusual safe. Each of the buttons must be pressed only once in the correct order to open it. The last button is marked F. The number of moves and the direction is marked on each button. Thus 1i would mean one move in, while 1o would mean one move out. 1c would mean one move clockwise and 1a would mean one move anti-clockwise. Which button is the first you must press?

TEST 8

6 Which of the boxes should be used to replace the question mark?

TEST 8 time limit 1 hour

A B

C D

E F

173

TEST 8

7 Discover the connection between the letters and the numbers. Which number should replace the question mark?

TEST 8 time limit 1 hour

K	16
Y	2
P	11
E	22
L	?

15	13	11
A	B	C
18	8	6
D	E	F

TEST 8

8 Which of the clocks continues this series?

A   B   C

D   E   F

175

TEST 8

9 Which of the numbers should replace the question mark?

	A	B	C	D
	7	5	3	4
	9	7	2	8
	6	8	7	2
	4	5	3	?

4 A	7 B
3 C	9 D
6 E	8 F

TEST 8

10 Each same symbol has a value. Work out the logic and discover what should replace the question mark.

τ	ψ	η	φ	63
φ	η	ψ	ψ	
τ	τ	τ	ψ	85
η	φ	η	η	?
58	**63**	**61**		

33	A		30	B		38	C

31	D		36	E		34	F

177

TEST 8

11 Move from ring to touching ring, starting from the bottom left corner and finishing in the top right corner. Collect nine numbers and total them. Which is the highest possible total?

TEST 8 time limit 1 hour

TEST 8

12 Scales one and two are in perfect balance. Which of these pans should replace the empty one?

TEST 8 time limit 1 hour

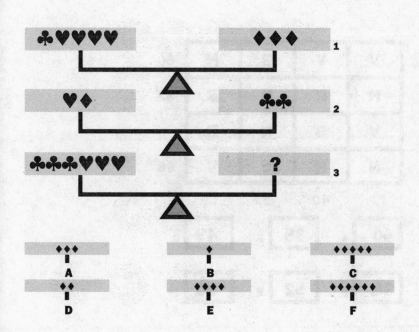

TEST 8

13 Each same letter has a value. Work out the logic and discover what should replace the question mark.

TEST 8 time limit 1 hour

V	V	B	N	60
H	H	N	B	32
V	B	N	B	
N	H	V	V	66

40   ?

40 A   **35** B   **49** C

38 D   **52** E   **50** F

TEST 8

14 Here is an unusual safe. Each of the buttons must be pressed only once in the correct order to open it. The last button is marked F. The number of moves and the direction is marked on each button. Thus 1U would mean one move up, while 1L would mean one move to the left. Using the grid reference, which button is the first you must press?

TEST 8 time limit 1 hour

	A	B	C	D	E	F
1	3R	4R	2L	2D	6D	1L
2	1R	1U	4D	2R	F	3L
3	3D	3D	1L	4D	4L	1L
4	3R	1L	1U	2R	2L	1U
5	3U	3R	1R	2L	1D	5L
6	5R	2U	5U	4U	2U	2L
7	5R	1R	2L	2L	5U	2U

2B	4E
A	B

1B	5C
C	D

6F	7D
E	F

TEST 8

15 Which of the constructed boxes can be made from the pattern?

TEST 8

16 When rearranged the shapes will give a number. Which of the numbers is it?

(2) A
(9) B
(8) C
(3) D
(4) E
(5) F

TEST 8

17 Move from ring to touching ring, starting from the bottom left corner and finishing in the top right corner. Collect nine numbers and total them. Which is the highest possible total?

The grid of numbers is:

7	9	8	-3	7
5	8	-6	5	6
3	-7	7	8	-4
6	9	5	-2	8
-5	5	4	9	5

48	49	51	52	56	58
A	B	C	D	E	F

TEST 8

18 Which of the boxes should be used to replace the question mark?

TEST 8

19 Which of the slices should be used to complete the cake so that the top half matches the bottom half?

TEST 8 time limit 1 hour

TEST 8

20 Which square's contents matches D2?

TEST 8 time limit 1 hour

	A			B			C			D			
	■	3	C	D	▲	3	3	C	D	■	■	■	**1**
	D	▲	1	D	1	D	C	▲	▲	3	3	3	
	1	3	1	C	C	1	▲	■	1	3	▲	C	**2**
	■	■	■	D	D	■	1	1	1	▲	■	3	
	C	3	3	3	▲	3	C	3	C	▲	3	3	**3**
	▲	■	▲	▲	1	▲	▲	C	1	3	▲	C	
	■	■	1	▲	C	▲	1	C	▲	1	C	3	**4**
	▲	C	1	▲	D	▲	■	▲	1	■	1	■	

D4 A	**C1** B
B1 C	**B2** D
A3 E	**C2** F

187

TEST 8

21 When the tiles in this square are rearranged a logical pattern will emerge. Which of the tiles should be used to complete the square?

9	1	6	5	
9	6	3	4	
9	8	1	6	8
1	2	7	7	7
2	9	5	2	3

A
1
3

B
5
3

C
4
2

D
2
4

E
3
1

F
1
1

TEST 8

22 Discover the connection between the letters and the numbers. Which number should replace the question mark?

TEST 8 time limit 1 hour

W	4	S
J	6	D
O	3	L
R	10	H
V	?	K

4	16	8
A	B	C
11	3	15
D	E	F

TEST 8

23 Here is an unusual safe. Each of the buttons must be pressed only once in the correct order to open it. The last button is marked F. The number of moves and the direction is marked on each button. Thus 1i would mean one move in, while 1o would mean one move out. 1c would mean one move clockwise and 1a would mean one move anti-clockwise. Which button is the first you must press?

TEST 8 time limit 1 hour

TEST 8

24 Which of the clocks continues this series?

TEST 8

25 Start at 2 and move from circle to touching circle. Collect four numbers each time. How many different routes are there to collect 39? A reversed route counts twice.

```
            16
         13  13  8
      13  13  16  13  16
   16  8  13  2  8  8  8
      13  13  13  16  16
         16  8  16
            13
```

```
   5      10
   A       B

   8       9
   C       D

   6       7
   E       F
```

TEST 8

26 Scales one and two are in perfect balance. Which of these pans should replace the empty one?

TEST 8 time limit 1 hour

193

TEST 8

27 Which shape is missing from this series?

TEST 8

28 Which circle should replace the empty one?

TEST 8 time limit 1 hour

29 Which triangle continues this series?

TEST 8 time limit 1 hour

TEST 8

30 Insert the correct mathematical signs between each number in order to resolve the equation. What are the signs?

TEST 8 time limit 1 hour

53		35		2		4		16	=	4

A ✕ ✕ ✕ ÷

B + − ✕ ✕

C − − ✕ ÷

D − + − ✕

E ÷ ✕ − −

F + − ✕ ÷

197

ANSWERS

TESTS 1–8

TEST 1 ANSWERS

1 F. On each row A + B + C = D.

2 D. $\Omega=5$, $\Xi=2$, $\Psi=4$, $Z=3$.

3 F.

4 E.

5 B. The numbers in the first triangle total 3, the second 4 and so on.

6 B. The alphabetical value of each letter is placed next to it.

7 C.

8 C. Each row totals 10.

9 B. The hour hand moves forward two hours each time.

10 E.

11 F.

12 D. When completed the box reads the same both down and across.

13 C.

14 D.

15 F.

TEST 1 ANSWERS

SCORE	RESULT
15	Strong Mensa Material
14	Strong Mensa Material
13	Strong Mensa Material
12	Highly Impressive
11	Impressive
10	Very Good
9	Good
8	Keep up the Hard Work
7	Keep up the Hard Work
6	Room for Improvement
5	Room for Improvement

TEST 2 ANSWERS

1 F.

2 A. ♣ = 6, ♥ = 5, ♦ = 2.

3 F.

4 E.

5 C. Each double section totals 10.

6 B. Two series lead from 1 to 16.

7 C.

8 D. Deduct row 2 from row 1 to give row 3.

9 C.

10 E.

11 E. On each row the two squares to the left total 9, as do the two to the right.

12 F. The numbers in the triangles total 4, 6, 8, 10 etc.

13 C.

14 A. The alphabetical value of each letter is placed next to it.

15 A.

TEST 2 ANSWERS

SCORE	RESULT
15	Strong Mensa Material
14	Strong Mensa Material
13	Strong Mensa Material
12	Highly Impressive
11	Impressive
10	Very Good
9	Good
8	Keep up the Good Work
7	Keep up the Good Work
6	Room for Improvement
5	Room for Improvement

TEST 3 ANSWERS

1   C. $\alpha=4$, $\beta=7$, $\chi=5$, $\delta=8$.

2   A. ♣ = 2, ♥ = 1, ♦ = 3.

3   E.

4   B. Each of the four columns of numbers totals 15.

5   C. 4a in the inner ring.

6   D. The numbers on each row total 9.

7   A. A large triangle added to the nearest small triangle will give the middle number.

8   E. Each double section is added together. Reading clockwise from 2 + 1, the totals increase by one each time.

9   B.

10   E.

11   D.

12   F. Each double section totals 13.

13   A. On each row the first figure minus the second figure plus the third figure gives the fourth.

14   E.

15   E. The first row plus the second row gives the third row.

16   C. The box now reads the same down and across.

17   B.

18   E.

19   E. ♣ = 8, ♥ = 6, ♦ = 7.

20   D. The hour hand moves forward two hours, then three hours, then four hours etc.

204

TEST 3 ANSWERS

SCORE	RESULT
20	Strong Mensa Material
19	Strong Mensa Material
18	Strong Mensa Material
17	Highly Impressive
16	Highly Impressive
15	Impressive
14	Impressive
13	Very Good
12	Very Good
11	Good
10	Good
9	Keep up the Hard Work
8	Keep up the Hard Work
7	Room for Improvement
6	Room for Improvement
5	Room for Improvement

TEST 4 ANSWERS

1 A.

2 B.

3 B. In each triangle the bottom two numbers, when added together, give the top number.

4 F. The hour hand moves back four hours each time.

5 C. On each row A + B - C = D.

6 E.

7 D.

8 A. When completed the box reads the same both down and across.

9 C.

10 C.

11 D.

12 D.

13 A. $\alpha=6, \beta=3, \chi=7, \delta=10$.

14 B.

15 D.

16 F. A large circle minus the nearest small circle will give the middle number.

17 A.

18 B. Reading clockwise, the numbers relate to the number of line forming the shape in the previous sector.

19 C. The first row plus the third row gives the second row. in the middle.

20 E. The alphabetical positions of the letters are placed together in the middle.

TEST 4 ANSWERS

SCORE	RESULT
20	Strong Mensa Material
19	Strong Mensa Material
18	Highly Impressive
17	Highly Impressive
16	Highly Impressive
15	Impressive
14	Impressive
13	Very Good
12	Very Good
11	Good
10	Good
9	Keep up the Hard Work
8	Keep up the Hard Work
7	Room for Improvement
6	Room for Improvement
5	Room for Improvement

TEST 5 ANSWERS

1 B. 2c in the inner ring.

2 B.

3 A. Reading clockwise, the number in the sector is the alphabetical value of the letter in the previous sector.

4 F.

5 F.

6 C. Each column totals 8.

7 E.

8 B. From the 1, the numbers increase in a spiral by missing out one number, then two numbers, then three numbers and so on.

9 C.

10 F.

11 B. Each double section is added together. These totals increase by two each time.

12 F. When completed the box reads the same both down and across.

13 D. The value of individual letters is irrelevant.
The total of the row of numbers must match the total of the column of numbers.

14 E.

15 A.

TEST 5 ANSWERS

16 E. On each row A - B - C = D.

17 B.

18 C. ♣ = 4, ♥ = 3, ♦ = 1.

19 D. 1o in the inner ring, between another
  1o and 5a.

20 F.

21 A. The left number plus the top number
  gives the right number in each triangle.

22 C. The alphabetical values of the letters are
  added to give the number in the middle
  space.

23 B. The minute hand moves forward ten
  minutes
  and the hour hand one hour on each clock.

24 F. Divide the square into four 2 x 2 blocks.
  The four numbers in each block total 20.

25 D.

26 A.

27 F.

28 A.

29 A.

30 E.

TEST 5 ANSWERS

SCORE	RESULT
30	Strong Mensa Material
29	Strong Mensa Material
28	Strong Mensa Material
27	Strong Mensa Material
26	Strong Mensa Material
25	Strong Mensa Material
24	Strong Mensa Material
23	Strong Mensa Material
22	Highly Impressive
21	Highly Impressive
20	Highly Impressive
19	Impressive
18	Impressive
17	Impressive
16	Very Good
15	Very Good
14	Good
13	Good
12	Good
11	Keep up the Hard Work
10	Keep up the Hard Work
9	Keep up the Hard Eork
8	Room for Improvement
7	Room for Improvement
6	Room for Improvement
5	Room for Improvement

TEST 6 ANSWERS

1 E. The sectors in the bottom half total
one higher than their opposite in the top
half.

2 C.

3 F.

4 B.

5 F. 2c in the inner ring with 2c on either side,
and 2c outside.

6 D. ♣ = 5, ♥ = 7, ♦ = 4.

7 F.

8 F. The third row plus the second row
gives the first row.

9 A. Start in the extreme left circle. The series
of arrows zigzags up and down with the
arrows pointing as follows: up, down, right,
left, down. This repeats.

10 D.

11 B. When completed the box shows the same
pattern both down and across.

12 F.

13 C.

14 A. Each double section is added together.
This double and its opposite have the same
total.

15 E. The middle circle and the two rings of
circles all total 24.

TEST 6 ANSWERS

16 D.

17 E. The alphabetical positions of the letters are found and the smaller is taken from the larger.

18 C. In each triangle the bottom two numbers are multiplied to give the top.

19 B. K=11, Λ=12, O=15, Π=16.

20 D. On each row A x B + C = D.

21 E. The hour hand moves forward one hour and the minute hand moves five minutes back each time.

22 E.

23 B. Opposite sectors total the same.

24 D.

25 B.

26 B.

27 C.

28 D.

29 C. Start in the top circle. The series of arrowszigzags across in a downward direction withthe arrows pointing as follows: right, left,up, up, down, left. This repeats.

30 E.

TEST 6 ANSWERS

SCORE	RESULT
30	Strong Mensa Material
29	Strong Mensa Material
28	Strong Mensa Material
27	Strong Mensa Material
26	Strong Mensa Material
25	Strong Mensa Material
24	Strong Mensa Material
23	Strong Mensa Material
22	Highly Impressive
21	Highly Impressive
20	Highly Impressive
19	Impressive
18	Impressive
17	Impressive
16	Very Good
15	Very Good
14	Good
13	Good
12	Good
11	Keep up the Hard Work
10	Keep up the Hard Work
9	Keep up the Hard Work
8	Room for Improvement
7	Room for Improvement
6	Room for Improvement
5	Room for Improvement

TEST 7 ANSWERS

1 D. The left number divided by the top
number gives the right number in
each triangle.

2 A.

3 E. The first row plus the second row gives
the third row.

4 C. Each double section is added together.
All double sections total 9.

5 E.

6 D.

7 D.

8 A. Reverse each row of numbers. Add the
second row to the third to give the first row.

9 B.

10 D. When completed the box reads the same
both down and across.

11 C.

12 C.

13 F.

14 A. All straight lines of five triangles total 22.

15 E.

TEST 7 ANSWERS

16 D.

17 E. In each triangle the left number increases by four, the right number decreases by three and the number at the top doubles each time.

18 D.

19 E.

20 A. 2a in the inner ring, between 1o and 1i.

21 C. $\phi=6, \gamma=7, \eta=8, \tau=20$.

22 E. When completed the box shows the same pattern both down and across.

23 D.

24 C. ♣ = 1, ♥ = 8, ♦ = 11.

25 E.

26 A. On each row A x B - C = D.

27 D.

28 F.

29 F. The alphabetical values of the letters are placed on opposite sides in the middle space.

30 C. The minute hand moves forward fifteen minutes and the hour hand moves back two hours on each clock.

TEST 7 ANSWERS

SCORE	RESULT
30	Strong Mensa Material
29	Strong Mensa Material
28	Strong Mensa Material
27	Strong Mensa Material
26	Strong Mensa Material
25	Strong Mensa Material
24	Strong Mensa Material
23	Strong Mensa Material
22	Highly Impressive
21	Highly Impressive
20	Highly Impressive
19	Impressive
18	Impressive
17	Impressive
16	Very Good
15	Very Good
14	Good
13	Good
12	Good
11	Keep up the Hard Work
10	Keep up the Hard Work
9	Keep up the Hard Work
8	Room for Improvement
7	Room for Improvement
6	Room for Improvement
5	Room for Improvement

TEST 8 ANSWERS

1 D. Each double section is added together. Totals of opposite sections are equal.

2 C.

3 E.

4 F. Reverse each row of numbers. Add the first row to the second to give the third row.

5 C. 2a in the inner ring between 2a and 1o.

6 C.

7 A. Reverse the alphabet and give each letter its value. For example A=26, B = 25.

8 D. The minute hand moves forward twenty-five minutes and the hour hand moves back four hours on each clock.

9 C. On each row A + B ÷ C = D.

10 F. η=8, φ=10, τ=20, ψ=25.

11 B.

12 E. ♣ = 7, ♥ = 5, ♦ = 9.

13 E. B=2, H=8, N=14, V=22.

14 D.

TEST 8 ANSWERS

15 E.

16 B.

17 A.

18 E.

19 C. Give the letters their value in the alphabet and add them to the numbers. The top half of the circle will total 50, as will the bottom half.

20 E.

21 C. When completed the box reads the same both down and across.

22 D. The alphabetical value of the letters to the right are subtracted from the left to give the number in the middle space.

23 D. 3a in the inner ring, with 5a on both sides.

24 A. The minute hand moves back five minutes, then ten minutes then fifteen and so on. The hour hand moves two forward, two back, two forward and so on.

25 B.

26 D. ♣ = 6, ♥ = 9, ♦ = 10.

27 A.

28 F. The number in the middle circle multiplied by the adjacent small circle gives the value in the large outer circle.

29 D. In each triangle the left number decreases by five, four, three, two and so on. The right number increases by three, four, five, six and so on. The number at the top is left plus right.

30 C.

TEST 8 ANSWERS

SCORE	RESULT
30	Strong Mensa Material
29	Strong Mensa Material
28	Strong Mensa Material
27	Strong Mensa Material
26	Strong Mensa Material
25	Strong Mensa Material
24	Strong Mensa Material
23	Strong Mensa Material
22	Highly Impressive
21	Highly Impressive
20	Highly Impressive
19	Impressive
18	Impressive
17	Impressive
16	Very Good
15	Very Good
14	Good
13	Good
12	Good
11	Keep up the Hard Work
10	Keep up the Hard Work
9	Keep up the Hard Work
8	Room for Improvement
7	Room for Improvement
6	Room for Improvement
5	Room for Improvement